MY VERY OWN SUCCULENT

WRITTEN BY BETSY E. CLARK
ILLUSTRATIONS BY STEFANIE T. GEYER

SPECIAL THANKS TO MEL AND BRYAN FOR
THEIR INSPIRATION AND PLANT WISDOM.

My Very Own Succulent

Copyright © 2020 Betsy E. Clark

ISBN: 978-0-578-79702-1

Names, characters, and places are products of the author's imagination.

Front cover image, illustrations, and book design by Stefanie Geyer.

Printed in the United States of America.

First printing edition 2020.

Anna saw her mother waving to her as she walked out of school.

"Mommy, Mommy!" said Anna,
"Today in school we learned how
plants grow."

2

"See, it is here in my picture," said Anna as she
showed her mother a drawing,
"Plants need air, water, sunshine, and soil."

"Look Mommy, I drew the sunshine and air going into the plant to help it make food."

"You can get food at the store to feed me, but plants can't do that. Plants have to make their own food."

"And, for a plant to be healthy and stand tall, it needs water just like I do. See these little legs that I drew under the plant? Those are called roots."

"Roots grow down in the soil to bring water and other healthy things into the plant."

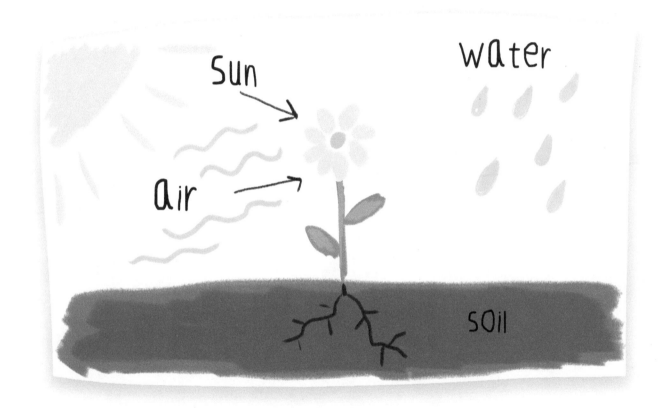

Sun

Air

water

soil

"My goodness Anna, you know a lot about how plants grow!" said her mother.

On the drive home from school, Anna said, "Did you know there is a special kind of plant that stores water? They are called succulents."

"My teacher said a succulent saves water inside its leaves, so it can have a drink when there is no rain."

"The water makes the leaves thick and sometimes puffy. My teacher showed us pictures, but I'd like to see a real one. Do we have a succulent plant in our yard?"

Her mother replied, "No we don't Anna, but let's go to the garden store this weekend and find a succulent of your own to put in our yard."

"Thank you Mommy, I hope we can find one," said Anna.

On the weekend, Anna and her mother visited the local garden store. When they entered the store, Anna asked the cashier, "Do you have succulent plants?"

"Yes we do," replied the helpful cashier,
"They will be on the right side of the back patio."

Anna and her mother walked to where there was a big sign that said "Succulents". "Oh Mommy," said Anna, "Look how many different kinds there are!"

SUCCULENTS

"Some have round leaves, some have triangle leaves, and some even have spikes. Look, this one is shaped like a star!"

Anna looked at all of them, trying to decide which one she wanted for her very own. Many were light green or dark green, but some were pink or blue.

She finally decided that she liked the dark green one with white stripes around each tall curving leaf.

"Mommy, what is the name of this one?" said Anna.

Her mother read the label, "That is named the Zebra Haworthia, because it looks like it has zebra stripes on it."

ZEBRA HAWORTHIA

Anna and her mother bought the succulent and some special soil. The cashier gave them a list with tips for caring for succulents.

"Have fun in the garden," said the cashier.

Anna smiled a big smile.

At home they planted the succulent in a larger pot to give it room to grow. "Anna, see how this pot has a hole in the bottom?" said her mother.

CACTUS
SOIL MIX

"The hole is important because succulents don't like to be wet. If the rain soaks the soil, the water can drain out the bottom hole to keep the succulent happy."

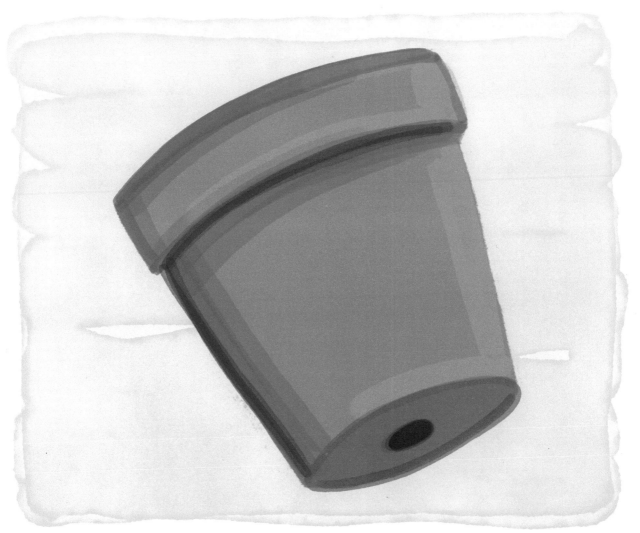

"Mommy," said Anna, "why did we buy special dirt at the garden store?"

"That is something I learned from the instructions," said her mother.

"Succulents need a loose soil that lets water drain to the bottom. We could make our own soil mix, but for our first succulent, I thought we would use the soil made by the store."

"Let's find a place in the yard where it is sunny and warm, but does not get too much hot sun," said her mother.

They looked around the yard and found a good spot that would be sunny in the morning and shady in the afternoon.

"Should I water it every day?" said Anna, holding the watering can. Her mother answered, "We will water it today and make sure the water flows out of the drain hole."

"We will check the soil with my moisture meter every two days. When the meter shows the soil is almost dry, we will add more water. After several days we will learn how often it needs water."

"What do we do when it rains or gets cold outside?" said Anna.

"If it rains a lot, but stays warm, we can move the pot under the shed roof where the rain won't drown it," said her mother.

"But in the winter, if there isn't enough sunshine or it gets too cold, we will bring the plant inside to keep it healthy."

"Instead of real sunlight, we can set up an indoor plant light to shine on the succulent until Spring."

33

Anna and her mother went inside to eat lunch. Anna turned around, smiled one more time at her new succulent, and said, "I can't wait to tell my teacher that I am caring for my very own succulent!"

TIPS FOR GROWING SUCCULENTS

PLANTING SUPPLIES

• Use a "cactus mix" potting soil or make your own mix.

• Use pots that have at least one drain hole and that are breathable. A good choice is TerraCotta.

LIGHTING NEEDS

• Succulents live best outdoors in bright indirect morning light.

• Place your plants where they get plenty of air, and are protected from the rain and cold.

• If your plants are indoors, give them enough light from a window or use an indoor plant light.

• Look up the ideal hardiness zone and lighting conditions for your plant on websites such as succycrafts.com.

WATERING

• Soak the soil until water comes out of the bottom of the pot. Toss out any water that collects in the saucer under the pot.

• Only water succulents when the soil is dry. A moisture meter is helpful.

• It is better to soak the soil at the base of the plant. Some succulents have a powdery coating on their leaves that is like sunscreen. If you water your succulents from the top, the water can wipe off this protective coating.

PLANTING OR POTTING

• When you place the plant in the soil, hold your succulent from the top and place your fingers under the leaves.

• Completely bury the root ball with soil. Then gently press on the soil around he plant. You can see videos of succulent planting on websites such as succycrafts.com.